Thinking Algebraically

With Numbers and Shapes

Student Activity Book
Level C

by
Jeane M. Joyner
and
Wade H. Sherard III

DALE SEYMOUR PUBLICATIONS
Pearson Learning Group

Hundred-Board Challenge

Each letter on this hundred board represents a different number. Remember, the number in the top left corner of a hundred board is 1. The number in the bottom right corner is 100.

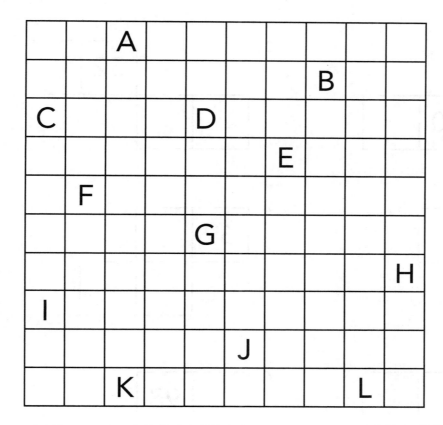

Use the hundred board above. Write the number value of each letter.

A = _____   G = _____

B = _____   H = _____

C = _____   I = _____

D = _____   J = _____

E = _____   K = _____

F = _____   L = _____

Hundred-Board Super Challenge

Decide if each of these shapes could fit on a hundred board. If a shape does not fit, move the number to another box so that it will fit. Fill in the missing numbers.

1.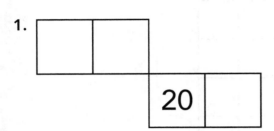

2.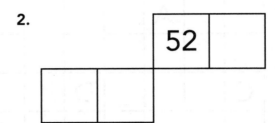

3.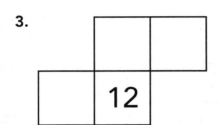

4.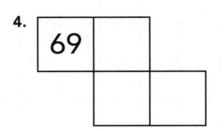

5.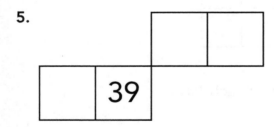

6.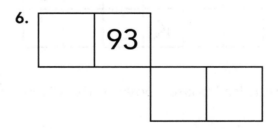

Thinking Algebraically, **Level C**

Three Coins in Your Pocket

1. You have three coins in your pocket. Each coin is a nickel or a penny. List the possible combinations of coins. Complete the chart. The first one is done for you.

Nickels	Pennies	Total Value
3	0	15¢
2		
1		
0		

2. Which combination of nickels and pennies is worth the most?

_____

3. Which combination of nickels and pennies is worth the least?

_____

4. Look at the chart. What patterns do you see?

_____

_____

_____

5. You have three coins in your pocket. Each coin is a nickel or a dime.
List the possible combinations. Complete the chart.

Nickels	Dimes	Total Value

6. You have three coins in your pocket. Each coin is a dime or a penny.
List the possible combinations. Complete the chart.

Dimes	Pennies	Total Value

Thinking Algebraically, Level C

An Apple a Day

1. You want to buy an apple that costs 35¢. You have a pocketful of quarters, dimes, and nickels. Find all the possible ways you could pay. Complete the chart.

Quarters	Dimes	Nickels
1	1	0
1		

2. You pay for the apple with only dimes and nickels. You use more dimes than nickels. How many of each coin do you use?

3. Can you pay for the apple using only three coins? Explain.

_____

_____

_____

I. O. U.

1. You owe your friend 40¢. You have only dimes and nickels in your pocket. What combinations of these coins could you use to pay back the money? Make a list.

Dimes	Nickels

2. How many dimes and nickels could you use to pay your friend if you use more dimes than nickels?

3. How many dimes and nickels could you use if the number of nickels is two times the number of dimes?

4. Suppose you had seven pennies, some nickels, and some dimes. What is the greatest number of coins you could use to make 40¢? Tell how many of each coin.

Exactly Five

Can you make each of the following money amounts with exactly five coins? Write *yes* or *no*. If the answer is yes, list the coins. If the answer is no, explain why. Make charts if you need to.

1. 32¢

_____

2. 55¢

_____

3. 15¢

_____

4. 75¢

_____

5. 46¢

Number Clues

Read each clue. Then write what the numbers could be.

1.

Clues	Numbers
The number is between 15 and 25.	
The number is even.	
The sum of the digits is 4.	

The number is _____.

2.

Clues	Numbers
The number is less than 30 but greater than 15.	
The number is greater than two tens.	
You can count by 5s to get to the number.	

The number is _____.

3.

Clues	Numbers
It is a two-digit number.	
Both digits are the same even number.	
The number is more than the value of three quarters.	

The number is _____.

4.

Clues	Numbers
The number is between 5×5 and 10×5.	
The sum of the digits is 10.	
The number is greater than the value of nine nickels.	

The number is _____.

What Is the Number? (A)

Use the clues to find each number.

1. It is a two-digit number.
It is less than 6×5.
It is an odd number.
The sum of the digits is 5.

What is the number? _____

2. The digits in this number are the same.
It is an odd number.
The sum of the digits is greater than one dozen.
It is less than the value of 8 dimes.

What is the number? _____

3. Count by 9s and you will say this number.
It is a multiple of 6.
It is greater than 20 and less than 50.

What is the number? _____

4. This number has one digit.
It is an even number.
The number is equal to the value of the same number of
    nickels and pennies.

What is the number? _____

5. The number is less than 90.
   Count by 5s and 8s and you will say this number.
   It is greater than the value of 5 dimes.

   What is the number? _____

6. The number has three digits.
   It is a multiple of 10.
   The number is equal to the value of six quarters.

   What is the number? _____

7. The number is greater than the value of three dimes and
      less than the value of 12 nickels.
   You can make it using three different coins.
   You can make this number using four of the same coin.

   What is the number? _____

8. The number is greater than 10 but less than 50.
   Count by 2s and you will say this number.
   You can make it using two of the same coin.

   What is the number? _____

What Is the Number? (B)

Use the clues to find each number.

1. The number is greater than 30 but less than 60.
Count by 3s and you will say this number.
It is an even number.
The product of the digits is 32.

What is the number? _____

2. The number is greater than 100 and less than 200.
Count by 10s and by 5s and you will say this number.
The number is greater than the value of 15 dimes.
The sum of the digits is evenly divisible by 8.

What is the number? _____

3. The number is between 24 and 58.
Count by 3s and you will say this number.
It is an odd number.
The number is a multiple of 9.
The number is less than the value of three dimes.

What is the number? _____

Thinking Algebraically, **Level C**

More Number Puzzles

Use the clues to find each number.

1. This number is greater than the value of four quarters.
It is less than the value of six quarters.
Count by 5s and you will say this number.
The sum of the digits is 9.

What is the number? _____

Change a clue so the answer is 125.

_____

_____

2. This number is less than the number of inches in a yard, but greater
than the number of inches in a foot.
Count by 4s and you will say this number.
It is greater than the number of ounces in a pound.
The sum of the digits is the number of cups in 5 pints.

What is the number? _____

Change a clue so the answer is 24.

_____

_____

3. This number is between 15 and 75.
It is a multiple of both 4 and 6.
The sum of the digits is 6.
(Hint: There are two possible answers.)

What could the number be? _____

Change a clue so there is only one possible answer.

_____

_____

Write the Last Clue

Write the last clue for each puzzle. Be sure there is only one answer.

1. This number is less than 25.
Count by 4s and you will say this number.
The sum of the digits is odd.

_____

_____

What is the number? _____

2. This number is between 20 and 50.
The number is a multiple of 6.
Counting by 8s will not name this number.

_____

_____

What is the number? _____

3. This number is a multiple of 9.
It is between 50 and 90.
The number is less than the value of three quarters.

_____

_____

What is the number? _____

4. This number is less than 50 but greater than 20.
Count by 7s and you will say this number.
The number is divisible by 2.

_____

_____

What is the number? _____

5. This number is less than 80.
It is divisible by 8.
The sum of the digits is an even number.
The number is a multiple of 6.

_____

_____

What is the number? _____

6. This number is less than 130.
The number has 3 digits.
The number is divisible by 5.

_____

_____

What is the number? _____

Writing Three-Clue Puzzles

Think of your own number puzzles. Write three clues. Be sure there is only one answer.

1. _____

   _____

   _____

   What is the number? _____

2. _____

   _____

   _____

   What is the number? _____

3. _____

   _____

   _____

   What is the number? _____

How Many Legs?

One turkey has 2 legs. Complete the chart.

1.

Number of Turkeys	1	2	3	4	5	6	7
Number of Legs	2						

2. Describe the patterns you see in the chart.

_____

_____

_____

Use the chart to complete each sentence.

3. Eight turkeys have _____ legs.

4. Nine turkeys have _____ legs.

5. Ten turkeys have _____ legs.

One dog has 4 legs. Complete the chart.

6.	Number of Dogs	1	2	3	4	5	6	7
	Number of Legs							

7. Describe the patterns you see in the chart.

_____

_____

Use the chart to complete each sentence.

8. Eight dogs have _____ legs.

9. Nine dogs have _____ legs.

10. Ten dogs have _____ legs.

One grasshopper has 6 legs. Complete the chart.

11.	Number of Grasshoppers	1	2	3	4	5	6	7
	Number of Legs							

12. Describe the patterns you see in the chart.

_____

_____

Use the chart to complete each sentence.

13. Eight grasshoppers have _____ legs.

14. Nine grasshoppers have _____ legs.

15. Ten grasshoppers have _____ legs.

Thinking Algebraically, Level C

16. One octopus has 8 legs. Predict what the pattern in the chart below will be.

_____

_____

Complete the chart.

17.

Number of Octopuses	1	2	3	4	5	6	7
Number of Legs							

Use the chart to complete each sentence.

18. Eight octopuses have _____ legs.

19. Nine octopuses have _____ legs.

20. Ten octopuses have _____ legs.

21. Patterns help you to make predictions. Write some examples.

_____

_____

_____

_____

Grasshoppers and Turkeys

Use the pictures to answer each question. Make a chart if you like.

1. How many legs are there on three turkeys and one grasshopper?

2. How many legs are there on four turkeys and one grasshopper?

3. How many legs are there on five turkeys and one grasshopper?

4. How many legs are there on one grasshopper and six turkeys?

5. How many legs are there on one grasshopper and seven turkeys?

6. How many legs are there on two grasshoppers and eight turkeys?

Thinking Algebraically, Level C

More Grasshoppers and Turkeys

Use the pictures to answer each question. Make a chart if you like.

1. How many turkeys are needed to have 10 legs?

2. How many turkeys are needed to have 18 legs?

3. How many grasshoppers are needed to have 24 legs?

4. How many grasshoppers are needed to have 54 legs?

5. There are the same number of turkeys and grasshoppers. There are 24 legs in all. How many of each animal could there be? Show or explain your thinking.

Octopuses and Turkeys

Use the pictures to answer each question. Make a chart if you like.

1. How many legs are there on two turkeys and one octopus?

2. How many legs are there on four turkeys and one octopus?

3. How many legs are there on three octopuses and ten turkeys?

4. How many octopuses are needed to have 40 legs?

5. There are 30 legs. There are the same number of octopuses and turkeys. How many of each animal are there? Show or explain your thinking.

Thinking Algebraically, Level C

The Same Number of Legs

Complete each sentence. Use the pictures to help you.

1. Three dogs have the same number of legs as _____ turkeys.

2. Two grasshoppers have the same number of legs as _____ dogs.

3. _____ dogs have the same number of legs as one octopus.

4. _____ turkeys have the same number of legs as four grasshoppers.

5. Six octopuses have the same number of legs as _____ grasshoppers.

6. Four dogs have the same number of legs as two _____.

What Do You Know?

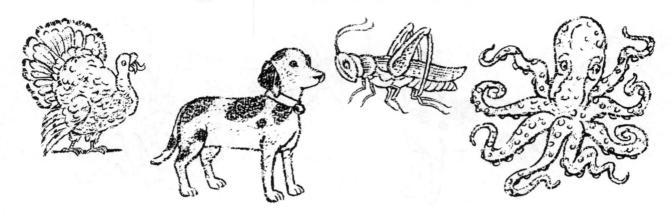

Use numbers to complete each sentence.

1. _____ dogs have the same number of legs as _____ turkeys.

2. _____ octopuses have the same number of legs as _____ dogs.

3. _____ turkeys have the same number of legs as _____ grasshoppers.

4. _____ dogs have the same number of legs as _____ grasshoppers.

5. _____ turkeys have the same number of legs as _____ octopuses.

Number of Legs Challenges

Complete each sentence. Use the pictures to help you.

1. Four dogs have the same number of legs as _____ octopuses and

_____ turkeys.

2. _____ octopuses have the same number of legs as 12 turkeys and

_____ grasshoppers.

3. There are 26 legs. There are some octopuses and some turkeys. How many of each animal could there be? Show or explain your thinking.

Sticker Book (A)

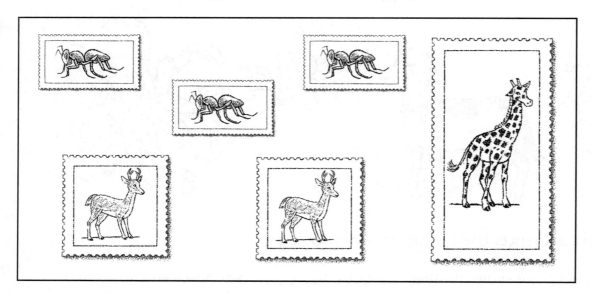

Use the sticker page to solve each problem.

1. How many stickers are there on 2 pages? Write an equation.

2. How many stickers are there on 4 pages? Write an equation.

3. How many deer stickers are there on 3 pages?

4. How many giraffe stickers are there on 5 pages?

5. You have 10 deer stickers. How many pages can you fill?

6. You have 12 ant stickers. How many pages can you fill?

Sticker Book (B)

Use the sticker page to solve each problem.

1. How many stickers are there on 8 pages? Write an equation.

2. How many stickers are there on 10 pages? Write an equation.

3. How many rabbit stickers are there on 7 pages?

4. How many hawk stickers are there on 4 pages?

5. You have 20 giraffe stickers. How many pages can you fill?
Will there be any stickers left over?

6. You have 12 rabbit stickers and 10 hawk stickers. How many pages can
you fill? Will there be any stickers left over?

Sticker Book (C)

Use the sticker page to solve each problem.

1. How many stickers are there on 9 pages? Write an equation.

2. How many zebra stickers and panther stickers are there on 8 pages? Write an equation.

3. You have 24 panther stickers. How many pages can you make?

4. How many zebra and giraffe stickers are there on 3 pages?

5. You have 20 panther stickers. How many pages can you fill? Will there be any stickers left over?

6. You have 18 zebra stickers. How many pages can you fill? Will there be any stickers left over?

Thinking Algebraically, Level C

Shape Riddles (B)

Solve each riddle. Use pattern blocks.

RIDDLE THREE

    Clue 1   There are fewer than seven blocks in the bag.

    Clue 2   There are two colors of blocks.

    Clue 3   Each shape is a quadrilateral.

    Clue 4   There is one more trapezoid than there are squares.

    Clue 5   There are two squares.

The answer is _____

_____

RIDDLE FOUR

    Clue 1   There are six blocks in the bag.

    Clue 2   There are the same number of each block.

    Clue 3   Two of the blocks are squares.

    Clue 4   There are no trapezoids.

    Clue 5   Two kinds of blocks are not quadrilaterals.

The answer is _____

_____

Write Your Own Riddle

Create your own pattern block riddle. Write five clues. Remember, the number of pattern blocks of each kind should not be found out until the last clue.

Clue 1

_____

_____

Clue 2

_____

_____

Clue 3

_____

_____

Clue 4

_____

_____

Clue 5

_____

_____

The answer is _____

_____